WHEN I WAS BORN

The journey of transition from self-employed to entrepreneur

Mehdi Sororiyan

The journey of transition from self-employed to entrepreneur

It was in the middle of the year 2009, and I was just beginning to settle into the new place I'd moved to... Vancouver. I started to look for work, handing out my resume to different stores and job sites, in the hopes that someone would employ me. Although, back home, I was a business owner and I still had that drive to try and work for myself again, and not just somebody else.

WHEN I WAS BORN

So, I was in the middle of the streets handing out my resume, but my mind was elsewhere: could I open my own business here? How could I do it? I was in a different country, using English as my second language, and I also don't know what opportunities surround me in this great country.

Here, I felt that I had big competitors in the form of big companies who can — and would — destroy me and my business in the blink of an eye. Having worked in the jewelry industry for a while, I made the effort of going to every jewelry store I could find in the area, to drop my resume off to the manager. Even if I wanted to start my own business, I had to get the money needed in order to live first. I do have to say, my first interview was awful, but it is just part of the process of learning about jobs and the hiring process in another country. I was learning about paper and online resumes, using my network and my networking skills, how recommendations and references help - but there was something else! There was something so incredibly wrong, I felt it in my gut.

It was that I wasn't happy with the activities I was pursuing, especially searching for jobs. The one desire burning in my mind and my gut was the desire to work for myself and no one else. I had pushed it deep down, buried it while I searched for work, but the feeling was still there.

For me, every morning begins with checking my inbox to see if any of the vacancies I had applied for had replied: there was none.

I managed to get a couple of second interviews for various positions, but especially in sales. While I was attending these interviews, I began searching for a degree in an electrical field, and also looking at a new career in an electrical field or starting a new career in biomedicine. As days passed by, the mere thought of getting a job filled me with dread from the bottom of my heart. I could hear the voice in my head, addressing my worst fears and bad thoughts:

So...what? Do you want to work for someone else for the rest of your life, just having a normal job, working every day and for what? Was this the reason you moved to another country? Is this it? Is this your life's purpose?

These words echoed around my head so many times each day, it was like it all blurred into one.

WHEN I WAS BORN

Then one Monday night, it was different. After facing the challenges of the day, I decided to relax by lying on the couch and reflecting (not that this was the most relaxing thing I could have done), in the last couple of months in my head. I was about to get back into my usual cycle of negative thought patterns when my phone rings. It was one of my closest friends, Xander; we'd been friends since high school, we've worked together sporadically over the years, from in shops as young teens, to right up until a few years ago, where we ended up working in the project together - just before I became a business owner. So, I picked up the phone and answered.

"Hey, how are you?" Xander said, really chatty and bubbly. I really wasn't feeling the same way right now.

"I'm fine, how are you? What's up?" I reply, closing my eyes, ready for an hour-long conversation.

"I'm okay. I was just wondering, are you still looking for a job?" I open my eyes at his words, my heart beating slightly faster. Is this real?

"I'm still looking for one, yeah. Why?"

"I might have one for you - well, it's not a job exactly. But I believe it's what you're looking for." I sat up on the couch: he had my full attention.

"Can you give me more details? I'm interested, so what should I do? Do you need my resume?" I tried to keep the excitement out of my voice, but I knew it hadn't worked. I was posing all sorts of questions to him that came to my mind until he stopped me.

"You don't need anything for now. Just wear something smart, and I'll come to pick you up tomorrow for a business meeting at my house at 6:30 pm. Have a great night, I'll see you tomorrow, okay?."

I said my goodbyes and let my phone drop onto the couch. The fire that I had tried so hard to quench for months has now been fueled. And I can't put it out - I don't want to put it out.

*Sleeping posed very difficult that night. I didn't get to sleep until at least midnight, but when I opened my eyes the next morning, it was exactly 5 am. It wasn't a groggy wake up either, even though I'm never awake so early. It was because today was the day. I had a few vivid dreams that the more I started to wake up, the less I remembered of them until it was just a quote: "dream is not that you see in sleep, **dream** is something that does **not** let **you** sleep."*

The day dragged as I tried not to count down the seconds until 6 pm. When he knocked, I was already by the door in my suit.

We made small talk until we got into the car, but that was when he fell silent. I wasn't okay with him staying silent. Firstly, it's unusual for him not to talk so little and, secondly, he was supposed to tell me about my new career. I wanted to know a lot more about the opportunity, just in case, it's not something I wanted to do. Instead, Xander's acting like a driver who's sole duty tonight was to drive me there and remain silent —

although he's not, he's one of my closest friends. All the way there, he kept being silent and didn't talk to me. I felt it was quite strange and uncharacteristic for him to keep doing this the entire journey.

I don't remember much of the meeting; I vaguely recall going through a presentation that I can only remember a couple of sentences and words from - like making money, team-building, opportunity, finance and... my favorite.. ...entrepreneur. It all sounded quite interesting, and I felt motivated and excited about this opportunity.

So, I jumped straight in with all the enthusiasm I had. I'm sure I did ask questions, but I can't recall what they were, or the answers. I do remember calling my wife that night so I could get my Social Insurance Number (SIN), which I needed to register. This was when my wife turned around and asked a big question: do you trust them? Do you trust them enough to give them this information?

I stopped her there, promising to tell her all about it and answer her questions when I'm settled back at home. So, she gave me the number, and with the help of my friend and another guy who seemed to be a business coach and in charge of the office, I ended up registering!

My new mentor said: "Be in the office for 9 am tomorrow morning; it is the first day of your business."

Amongst my excitement, I was also feeling a bit clueless. "Wait, but I have a lot of questions."

"I'm sure you do," he replied, "Most of your questions will be answered through the process of your business. Now, that's enough. Go home and get some rest, I will see you tomorrow morning."

.So my friend drove me back home, the journey made in silence. I had a niggling thought that was trying to get out, and it was the big question my wife had asked me beforehand. Could I trust them?

When we pulled up, my wife was waiting at the door for me; I could tell by her face that she wasn't pleased. I said goodbye to my friend and walked towards her, waiting for her mouth to open and unleash a torrent of questions at me. It happened before I even reached the door.

Listening to them, I had no choice but to answer with "I don't know," which only served to fuel her rage.

All I knew was the company name, and I didn't even want to remember that because my wife decided to search for it on the internet. There are many bad comments and reviews on Google, with comments like "it's a scam", "the business doesn't work" and "they are a bunch of liars." This didn't make things any better.

When we got inside, the real shouting began. She stopped in the hallway and yelled: "You don't know what you've got yourself into. How can you be so blind?" And with that, she stormed off to bed.

A few hours later, I tiptoed into bed, desperately trying not to think about tomorrow, but it didn't work. I spent half the night awake and staring up at the ceiling, listening to the occasional car speed up on the road outside.

Day 1

Confusion

I managed to get a few hours of sleep, before I woke up at 5 am, out of fear for what was going to happen today. I was wide awake which was unusual for me. It usually takes me ages to feel awake in the mornings. I was dreading going into the office.

I managed to eat a half a slice of toast, before dropping my son at the daycare, and my wife at the store where she worked, before heading to my new office for my first day. On the drive over to the office, I tried calming myself down, talking to myself, criticizing myself for the night before. I shouldn't have been so excited and naive to not question things, or search the company name at the very least.

When I entered the office building, my trainer was waiting for me with a friendly smile in the reception area.

"Hi, there."

"Hi, how are you?" I replied.

"I'm fine, but I bet you're not quite. I'm sure you're a bit confused after last night." He got straight to the point. I was surprised he knew how I was feeling.

"How do you know?"

He shrugged. "Eh, it's normal to feel that way, especially when you don't know much about the job. But there's no need to worry. Now, let's begin."

Gesturing to follow him, we leave the reception area; I smile at the receptionist on the desk, and she smiled back, before resuming her phone conversation. He led me down a small corridor and turned right after a minute or so, into a vacant, small meeting room. It had a whiteboard on the wall opposite the door, the sturdy wooden table was in the middle of the room, with six chairs around it. On the table was a jug of water and six glasses stacked neatly in the middle. The mentor strode towards the whiteboard, turned around and said:

"Help yourself to the water." So I took one of the glasses and poured myself some water, wishing that it was coffee.

He smiled, a big wide toothy grin as he came over to the table, sat down, and handed me the folder that he had in his hands and said:

"This is the Business Welcome Package."

I took the folder from him and questioned him. "...Business package?"

"I am going to explain. We will go through it all together, and go through all the steps. There are many steps, and there's a reason behind every one of them."

Looking at how thick the folder was, I asked: "Are these steps and procedures for just this business?"

"Yeah they are steps for this business, but most of them are similar to how other businesses work, so it shouldn't be difficult. What's your working background again?"

"I'm a business owner," I said proudly, growing slightly taller as I lifted my head up.

"A business owner or self-employed?" My mentor smiled.

"Business owner; I had my own business. I employed two people to work with me, and I was my own boss, in charge of everything: hiring, communications with suppliers, firing, customers, you name it." I wondered whether he listened to me before, and as much as I had my own, more important questions to ask, I was the one being grilled.

"What would happen to the business if you weren't there? What would it be without you?"

"My business without me that would be impossible! Everything and everyone there depends on me." My patience was wearing slightly thin now. I rein it in, and took an inaudible deep breath and let it out slowly.

The guy continued. *"Do you have anyone that can take on your position and replace you?"*

"Forget that nobody can work like me! Nobody else can do what I can do," I threw my hands up in the air.

"So," this guy was relentless. *"You are self-employed, not a business owner. Your business has no system."*

Giving in, because I was clearly getting nowhere by showing my agitation, I said: *"Can you explain more?"*

"Yes, let's start with the difference between being self-employed and being a business owner, then talk about putting a system in place. Does that sound good to you?"

I nod. "Great." He got up from the meeting table and turned his attention to the whiteboard on the wall. He started to draw. I watched in silence.

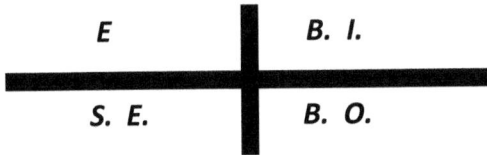

E	B. I.
S. E.	B. O.

"This concept was created by Robert Kiyosaki. So the E is for the employee; it is the beginning of the journey of our job and it is the person who works for the organization and gets paid for doing so — it's as simple as that. You get paid for your labor, your knowledge, and your skills. As you know, an employee can be in any position, from the lowest in the company to the highest roles, like the Chairman or Vice President, CEO, CFO, etc. Their pay can be a wage (a fixed amount paid) or based on a commission and bonuses — or a combination of both."

I nod periodically as I scribbled in the notebook that I brought with me. I still wasn't sure what job I'm supposed to be doing. I snapped out of my thoughts and back to the talk, I was getting.

"The employee's responsibility is to fulfill all of the duties of their position; the organization is not built around, so there if they're not fulfilling their role or they leave, then somebody else could cover or replace them. So, there's not that much flexibility within the role as they are bound by the rules of the organization.

"With self-employment, as the name shows, you are employed in your own business, which gives you more flexibility, but that comes with more responsibility. They are the core of their own business, and there is no business if they're not around. Most companies would rather outsource self-employed people rather than hire someone to do the same job in-house."

He finished and looked at me. I said: "So, what you're trying to say is that I was self-employed?"

"Yes, because your business has no meaning without you."

"So, what about the role of the business owner?"

"Now, we are getting to the interesting part," he smiled. *"I will explain, but let me have tea first! Would you like tea or coffee?"*

"Coffee, please, with milk, two sugars," I grinned at him. *Yes, I definitely need some more caffeine just to stay awake.*

As he left to make the drinks, I had a brief look around the tidy, clean office. He came back after a few minutes and placed a mug of coffee on the table for me; he still held his tea. Returning to near the whiteboard, he continued the talk.

"At the stage of the business owner, you may or may not still work in the business, but the biggest difference is that the business isn't stuck to you. You are not running the show of your business and it can go forward without you-"

"But that's impossible," I said, picking up my coffee. *"Who would do my job?"*

"System, my friend," he said, smiling again. *"If you do not have a system in place, you can't replace yourself with other people."*

"You're saying that if I have a system in place, then I can replace myself with somebody else who has similar skills and knowledge as I do, and they will keep the company running?"

"Precisely."

"Fair enough but what is the system?"

"The system is a manual of how your business runs, so without it, the business will fail because it would be full of errors and confusion amongst those who work there. So, in this business, we do have a system in place.

This began to make a bit more sense now. It was like a lightbulb had gone off in my head.

"Now I can see why it was always difficult for me to get a day off. It felt like all I ever did was work. It's because the only one who knows my business system is me, and I have a huge role in that system that no one else had. Okay, what should I do now to change this?"

"Hold on, wait. Do not be in a rush to change this so quickly. Take it step by step. Okay, I have good news and bad news for you. Which one do you want first?"

Slightly confused, I replied with: "The good news!"

"Okay, so in this business, we do have a system, and every part of it is written down and logged."

"That's great. Okay, so what about the bad one?"

"Implementing the said system really isn't easy at all."

"Okay, but why?" I was curious.

"So, let's have a look at your business. Most of the time in your business, at points you will change the people who you have working there, is that right?"

"Yes, that's correct."

"Well, that's why you used to have different results but here, we change the people based on the system, because our system has been proven and tested, so if you fail, it's not the system's fault, but the people's fault. If the people don't want to change, then change your people," he held out his arms, then continued. "It can be painful to say goodbye to the people in your business, but if you don't, then it's saying goodbye to growth and success. Changing

people is hard, I know, but you do feel a lot of joy after you've helped other people to achieve their goals. Helping them reach the future they wanted is one of the best feelings in the world, and one of the best things you can do as a leader and business owner. And, this brings me onto leadership; you need to have great leadership skills to be a business owner."

"What is leadership?" I asked, curiously.

"My god, we will have a long way to go! But I do love working with people who are curious and ask good questions. To have leadership skills, you need to lead a group of people to reach their goal."

"Oh, so like a manager?"

"No, no, no, being a manager is completely different; you control people and make them complete their tasks. Leadership is beyond management; you are their coach, their mentor, their teacher. In the leadership position, you love your people, you care about them, their success and their journey. And they follow you, not because they have to, but they want to. You inspire them to achieve more."

"Okay, so I'm a little confused; what's the difference between a coach, mentor, and teacher — I thought they were pretty much the same thing!"

The guy tipped his head back and laughed. "It's like we're in kindergarten! Okay, okay, I'll give a brief explanation before getting back to the main topic.

"A coach is someone who helps people to find their strength and abilities and teaches how to use them. They do this whether or not they have any experience within that area of coaching. They unlock the personal potential within someone, focusing on the here and now rather than the distant past or future. A mentor is an experienced and trusted advisor in that specialist area you want to discuss. They make themselves available to help, support and guide the lesser experienced person when they need, helping them to also succeed with their goals. The mentoring is related to the experience that the mentor has. A teacher is someone who helps students acquire knowledge, and inspires and encourages their pupils to achieve great things and follow their dreams and aspirations. The difference between a teacher and a coach is that you choose the destination that you want to go in. The coach helps you get to your goal, whereas with teaching, it is the teacher that chooses what the student learns."

"Thank you for taking the time to explain it," I said as I turned a page in the notebook. "You've opened my eyes today, that's for sure." I finished the rest of my coffee and put the mug down on the table.

"My pleasure. Now, the most important part of the four corners of business is the investors. An investor is someone who uses their money (or other people's money) to invest in a business that they think has a good chance of obtaining profit, with a bit of risk involved. So, you might be thinking, why or when do investors use fancy money? Well, if they project a high return on the money in comparison to the risk. They use the money to make more money for the investors, who sometimes prefer to use their credit and get a loan from the bank. Mostly, these investors have the type of mindset that has a more conservative approach to business; they are exposed to the bigger failure or bankruptcy." He took a deep breath, glanced at his watch and, continued.

"We are going to quickly look at the concept of risk. Do you know the meaning of risk?"

"No, taking risks isn't good. I don't take risks!" I panicked, unsure if I should have said that, so I added, "Am I correct in my thinking?"

"Not exactly, but I understand your thoughts and your feelings. Anyway, I must go to the bathroom, so I'll be right back." The guy put his empty mug down before heading out to the restroom.

For the next few minutes, I scribbled furiously in the book, coming up with how I can implement this advice into my own business. Though, every so often those doubts keep creeping back in. But I don't know the simple concept of business, how can I call myself a businessman? How long will it take to learn what is needed in order for me to call myself a businessman? Can I do this? How can I implement those concepts into practice? How can I become a real business owner?

I tried to erase those thoughts from my mind and think more positively as I scribble the notes down in my notebook. My thoughts turned to the other people working in the building. It's a pretty large building, and I passed

WHEN I WAS BORN

As he walked back into the room, he spotted me writing and said: "What are you writing about?"

"Nothing much," I replied. "Just a new business concept."

He came over to have a look at my scribbles. "These are not new concepts as a whole, but they're new to you. So," he claps. Where were we? Ah yes! Risk. First, do you know the meaning of the word? In the dictionary, it states that risk means a situation involving exposure to danger. This can help you to understand why people are so skeptical about taking risks and why they freak out about risks. It's because of the definition of the word, they don't try to understand the meaning behind it. If you take a look at life in general, and your life specifically, you will find that there are always some risks involved. What you will also find is that where there is a risk, there is a reward, and this goes for everything.

In the dictionary, the word 'rewards' means rewards given in recognition of one's service, effort, achievement or return or bad behavior."

He paused, and stared off into space for a moment, before snapping back to the here and now. Maybe he was *just reminded of something, I thought as he continued on. I'm starting to see that it can be okay to take a few risks ever so often.*

So, I focused back on my mentor, who continued to talk and educate me: "As I said, we should define and associate risks and rewards together because they go hand-in-hand. Everything in life has risks and rewards, and mostly it's the case of tending to the tasks that have bigger rewards — and the reward seems 'bigger' in comparison to the task. Being risky and taking risks isn't always a bad thing. If we predict a greater return compared to the risk factors that are involved, we find that the bigger rewards come after the biggest risks, not with small risks. As a business person, you have to draw your risks and rewards chart, and find the optimum point; at what point in the chart is the correlation of the reward to risk ratio in favor of us? I hope this is sounding a bit clearer to you about it all because it is linked with your daily, weekly, and yearly activities and goals." He paused to allow me to answer.

"Yes, it's much clearer now, I understand it a lot more."

He nodded towards me and carried on.

"Fantastic, so let's give an example: have you talked to your employees, especially those who are of lower rank about the risk in jobs? A lot of employees have the mindset that there is no risk with jobs; they will go and apply for jobs, get one and there is no risk. Actually, they are very wrong, there is always a lot of risks involved with jobs, whether it is employment, self-employment or ownership of the business. Okay now that we've looked at the concept like this, I want you to look at it from a different perspective.

"Do they have no risks in that job at all, or do the risks arise when it is known to them that somebody else can do their job and poses competition or a threat? Like if somebody else was to do the job for a lower cost, or can deliver better work. And answer this: have you ever seen an organization that states that when you're hired, you're there permanently, no questions asked?" I shook my head. *"Exactly. No job is guaranteed forever. Do they hire every person? Do they hire every day as well? What happened to the overflow of employees? If you're not performing well enough, a business can terminate your employment. So, you can see here that risk is an interesting factor, but understanding properly is the*

must-factor of life! Here is a quote that you should write down and try to remember.

> If you don't understand the risk you are in a higher risk.

Business owners and self-employed people have a lot of risks involved. We will speak more of that later. Anyway, " he glanced at his watch again, eyebrows raised. "I have talked for quite a while and it's now time for a break. Let's get lunch!"

I hadn't realized the time at all. It really has flown by today. I agreed on lunch and we set off out of the office to one of the nearby restaurants. It was a dimly lit, cozy place with friendly staff. We weren't waiting by the entrance long before one of the waitresses sat us down at one of the dark oak tables, as per my trainer's preference for a table in the corner, or as he called it "cozy corner".

Sitting in the corner of the restaurant by the window, we spot trees outside that are decorated with yellow trees, with the red leaves of maple trees slowly falling to the floor with every gust of wind.

We ordered our food with the waitress, made small talk before the food arrived, ate lunch and got ready to leave. It was an ordinary lunch, but a very pleasant one.

"Today's lunch is on me, please," I said as I got my wallet out of my jacket. *He agreed without much of an argument, so I paid up and we left. On the way back to the office, we talked mainly about his business experience — successes, failures, good and bad times and so on. As we got back to the meeting room, I pulled out my notebook as I sat down. Before he began again, he asked me:* "Why do you want to do this business? If you want me to be your mentor, then I need to make sure your 'why' is strong enough. It is the most important part of the process that makes sure you find a way to do everything and not give up at the first obstacle."

I listen, captivated.

"Running a business is like climbing the mountain to the peak. If you're climbing for fun, or to show off, then you will never reach the top. There are a lot of difficult conditions to face on the way up there: cold weather, cliffs, falling rocks, and much more — and you can't predict them all. Are you strong enough to survive the obstacles standing in your way?" My mentor grinned and continued: *"Right, on a blank piece of paper, write down at least five of your biggest 'whys'."*

I turned to a blank page in my notebook. Yes, I did have some already, but they were in my head; I started writing them down. My mentor carried on his speech, so I kept listening as I wrote down my 'whys'.

"Think of it this way: what are you going to fulfill by running the business? Some people do it for their family, their parents, kids, spouses, or for charities, to make a change (big or small) within the community and so on. As you can see, an example of a small goal is just to earn money and to go home, but a big goal, for example, would be to make a huge impact or change in the world. In my opinion, having both small and large goals is the best way to set your goals. If you have a big goal, these typically take a lot of time and a huge amount of work, effort, and sacrifices, but achieving them enables you to feel blessed and fulfilling. And the small goals may not take that much time, but achieving them guides you through the route to achieving your bigger goals, and gives you energy and motivation to stay on track, and get back to the game again and again. Do you understand what I am talking about?" He paused slightly, so I nodded at him. He then pressed on.

"I think this is it for today. We've got through a lot of information today, and you've done very well. So, if you take your task and complete it at home, then we can move onwards tomorrow. Okay, so I'll see you tomorrow at 9 am sharp with it completed."

I muttered in agreement as I finished my second glass of water and stuffed my notebook back into my bag. I stood up, tucked my chair under the table and turned to leave when he added:

"Make sure to do this with your family. Do you understand?"

"Why do this with my family?" I was confused. I paused, about to leave the room so I could hear what he was going to say.

"Of course, you must share this with your family. Running a business isn't, short-term, it's not just a small part of your life. You will need to discuss it with them as you want them on your side throughout your career, so include them from day one!"

And, with that being said, I left the room and walked back down the corridor, through the reception area and exit the building. I was extremely tired after that very intense first day, but for the first time as a whole, I felt a spark ignite inside of me. This was the right job for me, I could feel it.

Day 2

Who Is My
AVATAR

Despite being extremely tired from the lack of sleep from the night before, this night was just as bad. I was up most of the night, thinking about my 'whys' and I was surrounded by different feelings, like anxiousness, exhaustion, fatigue. When I woke from the little sleep I got, I realized that I had woken up late. I scrambled around the house, making sure that I had everything I needed before I had to leave. By the time I had reached the office, I was 20 minutes late. I've only ever been this late before once when I had an appointment to go to, and I couldn't make it on time. And once again, I didn't make it on time today either. It was only my second day; I felt extremely bad for doing this.

To make matters worse, my trainer was standing by the door with a tight-lipped smile etched into his face, and his finger pointing at the clock. I was in big trouble. Without another word, he turned on his heel and headed to the room we were in yesterday. I followed behind him and sat in the chair I did yesterday. I barely had time to get my notebook out when he turned to face me and began speaking.

"The first lesson today," he began. *"Is discipline, discipline, discipline; it is the basic factor of human success in life, careers, and relationships."*

I looked at the floor. "I'm sorry," I muttered, like an ashamed school kid being told off for being late.

"All of the journeys of being a businessman is full of tasks, and although there is no obligation to do them, it's an unspoken role that you have to do it. The same goes for being on time, and not late. Well, it's not just the fact that you need to be on time, you need to be in the office before everybody else - and I mean everybody. In your business, you are the first one who arrives at the office in the morning and you are the last one who leaves the office at the end of the day. It isn't just for everything. Do you get it? Being sorry doesn't do anything. If you don't learn to have discipline, you won't succeed in anything. In the business, you are the first one to get into the office and the last one to leave. Do you get it?"

I replied: "Yes, Mr. Trainer."

"There are lots of different definitions for discipline but the best I found is this:

> Discipline means doing something right when you are not obligated to

"Right," he clapped his hands together and headed inside. *"Let's begin on today's tasks. Have you done your work, the five reasons 'why'? If it isn't completed, we cannot move on."*

Without a word, I handed my paper over to him, who looked pleased.

"Do you have another copy you can put up somewhere so you can see them every day." He sat down at the table inside the office; I sat opposite him. *"Let's talk about your market then. Working on marketing is one of the hardest but best parts of your business. Lots of businesses fail because they don't know how to market themselves or*

their products or services. Your market is the people who use your service or product.

It used to be that people produced a service or product, they then found a market. On the other hand, the value of the service you offer to people or the product you deliver to them is your market, but the tables have turned recently, and now you have to identify a market before you come up with a product. So, who is your market? This is the second step, not to mention that you can now do both new and old methods."

"What do you mean by new and old methods?" I was full of questions.

"It means you can find a market and then build your products and service. Due to the market, you have a value proposition, so then you can find a market due to the product or service you are offering (or the value proposition). Let's name your product or service "value proposition", and the market as the "customer segment". It does not matter if you find your customer segment after your value proposition or before, because as a founder of a business you have to know your market

default; it means you have to know your customer segment in all aspects of their life which is directly or indirectly related to your value proposition. Darren Hardy, Founder of Success Magazine says: 'You have to be with the customer all day, being with them as they wake up in the morning till they go to the bed in the night even you should be in their night dreams as well."

I was very taken aback by this. "But I cannot do that, it's against privacy, I mean, what about washrooms; do I go there with them as well?"

My mentor howled with laughter. It was the afternoon when we started this conversation, and he found my remark hilarious for the remainder of the day. Once he'd stopped laughing, I said:

"I am joking, by the way! So, you want me to find out the customer's unspoken words, feelings, and factors that help them to decide on things? You want me to write it down today?" He nodded, before adding "though, for the rest of the day, I have to be in a meeting. You're more than welcome to stay in the office to do this task, but you can also go home to do it - as long as you complete this for today. All the homework isn't just a one-off, you can use it multiple times - it's lifetime homework. Over the

years, you will correct it, edit it, add to it partially or as a whole anytime in the future. It will help you more over the years as you grow and develop yourself and your business. Our job is done for today, grab a paper and you'll be free to go! They are on my desk! As I grabbed the paper on his desk, I was shocked by the questionnaire.

What is your customer AVATAR name?

I turned to him and asked, "What does this mean? I'm confused."

He answered with a big smile on his face: "Don't worry too much, I just wanted to show you how you should know your customer in detail and what you should know about them. The paper will help as there are detailed questions - see the back of the paper. Now, see you tomorrow morning, at 9 am sharp." With that, he left. I started to read the paper.

Your customer demographics

Age

Gender

Customer location

Gather/ Attend

Customer lifestyle

Income

Number of children

&

Describe one day of your customer in detail.

Day 3

Value Proposition

This Friday morning, I woke up at 7 am to organize the papers, drop my son and wife off as usual. Though this time, my son really didn't want to wake up, so I had to keep trying over and over again. He squealed "too dark" and proceeded to try and sleep again. I had to smile, for he meant that it's still dark outside, and therefore it wasn't time to wake up just yet. However, I managed to convince him to get out of bed (by making his favorite breakfast - scrambled eggs). Of course, by the time we left to get in the car, the sun had risen, though it was hiding behind white fluffy clouds. I managed to reach the office early this time before 9am. There were a few people in the building when I arrived, and after me, more started to come filing through to the biggest conference room, which can seat up to 20 people. There was a huge table, a projector screen, a whiteboard, and a coffee machine with many paper cups beside it. I explored the building more, and one other meeting room was in the hallway to the left, and there was one big kitchen used by everyone that had a silver microwave, refrigerator, and beautiful cherry wood cabinet. There was a dining table in the kitchen that everyone was allowed to sit at while they ate their food. I was thinking to myself, what if they don't want to eat at the table? Why is there a table in the kitchen, when people can bring their food to their desk in *their room? As it was approaching 9am, I wandered back round to my trainer's room.*

I entered my trainer's office and greeted him. "Good morning."

He looked up from the paperwork on his desk and said: "Hello, Mr. Entrepreneur how are you? Sleep well last night?"

I shook my head: "I've not slept well since Tuesday night. I've only been getting around four or five hours a night. I've not been able to go to sleep until late, but I end up waking up very early."

"That is quite normal, you are going to get used to it. Did you do the work?"

I handed him my work.

"Excellent, let's go to the next concept of 'value'. If you remember from the last two days, we have talked about the value: whether you choose your value based on the market or you have the market, then create the value.

"Value? What does it mean? For the service business I can understand but what if, for example, you sell goods like a watch, do you know the value you would give it?"

"Yes and no. With the service industry, you can understand if you sell goods like watches, what value to give it. It depends on the watches you sell. If you sell a regular watch, the value will be different than if you sell a higher-priced watch. It is being unique, having prestige, trading value for money for the customer is important. You can value a proposition that hits for a customer segment, then most of your job in the business is done. Yesterday, we were trying to find a customer segment that we were thinking that we have the value for the customer and, then know the customer. So if you know everything you need to know about your customer, then you can find out more about your market pain and gain."

"Pain and gain?" I wasn't so sure.

"Correct. Pain means everything. Everyone has pain in their life, career, and relationships."

"So, I have to invent the 'painkiller'?" I said with a smile.

"Yes, somehow! Your value to them should help in some way to give them less or no pain in particular parts of their life."

"Sounds great but what about gain?"

"Some organizations help people to live happier. In fact, their target market lives a more pleasant life by using their product or service."

Therefore by using your product, they are happier."

"So, gracious, for example, the value of that airline company is that they help their passengers to move between two locations faster and safer."

"Bingo! These are the two main values. There are the other side values as well, but first and foremost are traveling safe and fast! Sometimes there is not always a line between pain or gain, for example, the first day the airline was created, it was to relieve the pain of long travel, but not their service is somehow the cause for their passengers to gain a better lifestyle. That's why we can see flights take 20 minutes maximum! The one hour drive between two points, plus adding airport times, there is no

more pain in this section other than the gain. I hope I've helped you to understand the message. Have I?"

"I see," I pondered. "Yet somehow, I feel I need more help on the concept."

"That's fine! Let's go through the questionnaire step by step, and see what questions you need help with. I'm here to help you."

I pointed to all of the questions about value proposition, and pain and gain on the questionnaire.

> *What would make your customer happy? (gain)*
>> *What would make their life and job easier? (gain)*
>> *What is annoying or troubling your customers? (pain)*
>> *What is preventing them from getting the job done? (pain)*
>> *What can you offer your customers to help them achieve their gain? (gain creator)*
>> *How can you help your customer to relieve their pains? What problems can you eradicate? (pain reliever)*

See it's not hard as long as you go to the right process. Asking the right questions is the most important part of the entrepreneur.

> **Ability to ask the right question is the blood of entrepreneur**

I looked up from the questionnaire my mentor was going through with me; I looked at him and said: "How can I learn to ask the right questions for myself? I don't know much about most of the topics on here, so how can I ask the right questions? I'm unsure about a lot of this." I rubbed my eyes, trying to see if I could clear away my tiredness and looming headache. I felt like I couldn't focus at all; the information just wasn't sinking into my head. Instead, I found it slightly confusing. Meanwhile, my mentor found my questions highly amusing, it appeared, as he smiled and I could see he wanted to laugh.

"For now, you should just start the journey, I wouldn't worry about asking the right questions at the moment," he paused and chuckled to himself. He carried on. "Now, here's a question that I will put to you: how do you expect to know which questions are the correct ones, when you don't know the topics? It's not how it works, I'm afraid."

I saw his point, but I thought I'd explain further. "I was thinking, maybe questions like this: Where and how to find people? Are they reliable? Are those questions based on experience or theory? What were the results for people who used them before? So, questions like these, really."

He clapped his hands together in a non-sarcastic way; he actually seemed pleased.

"Congratulations, you've just learned how to ask the right questions. And that was just us talking about it, I'm impressed. So, what you need now is to put those questions to good use and get them to work. However, I believe that this is enough for today. So, for tonight, your challenge will be your value proposition. That means that you will work on these specific questions and bring them back first thing tomorrow morning. If you do have any questions in the meantime, please do not hesitate to contact me and ask. How does that sound to you? Is that good for you?"

I tilted my head slightly and looked back at him; I frowned. "Tomorrow? But tomorrow is Saturday. Why do I need to be here on Saturdays? Do you work Saturdays? It's very hard to work on Saturday. Most employees who work in the week have their whole weekends off. Do I get any days off? I'd like to see my family on my days off."

He took a deep breath and replied: "To your question about whether I work on weekends, then I should proudly say yes, I do work on weekends. The definition of an entrepreneur is completely different in comparison to an employee. That is why we work weekends, but anyway, this is definitely enough for today. But yes, we will discuss this entire point tomorrow, so make sure that you're here before 8:30 am this time; this is because we have our breakfast for half an hour with the other people in the office. So, this would be before our usual start at 9 am. On Saturdays, we have our communal weekly breakfast; everyone brings their own breakfast but brings enough to share with other people. Tea and coffee are already supplied from the office, so there's no need to bring tea bags or coffee granules. Bring something you want to eat. I'll be bringing a box of cereal tomorrow as I quite like cereal. Oh, and before I forget, please remember to do your homework tonight and bring that in as well, Mr. Entrepreneur."

I replied with: "Of course," as I put the questionnaire away into my bag, I said goodbye and waved to my trainer at the door, then headed back to my car. I was exhausted but I felt motivated to complete the task he's *set me for tonight. As I got into my car and drove out of the office car park, my mind wandered to tomorrow's early start and what I should bring to the weekly breakfast. I decided it was best to head to the supermarket on my way home to get some fruit for tomorrow. The supermarket strangely wasn't very busy tonight for a Friday. It didn't take me long to get the things I wanted, and I was home before I knew it.*

Day 4

Passion for business is a lifestyle, not a job

While my wife wasn't happy to see me go into work on a Saturday, she was pleased that I was working hard. She was shocked to see how early I had woken up on Saturday to get to work. I was up and ready to go with time to spare. The sun had only just risen, but it was peeping out from behind the clouds, so it too, was ready for the day to begin.

I made myself a bacon and egg sandwich and wrapped it in tin foil to keep it warm on the car drive to the office; I put my orange juice into a thermos mug to keep it cool and I packed the bananas, apples, and grapes that I purchased specifically for this morning.

As I put on my jacket and shoes to leave, I pecked my wife on the cheek and wished her a good day, and kissed my son on the forehead. He was too engrossed with playing with his little fire truck to properly notice; though I do not mind. I was hoping that I wouldn't spend all day in the office, so I could spend some time with them later.

I drove to the office, fully expecting everyone to be in terrible moods; it is Saturday after all, so why would they want to be instead of with their family? However, I was in for a big surprise, for when I stepped into the office, *everybody was energized and ready to start the day. I could feel the positive energy in the building and I hadn't even said hello to anyone yet.*

As I walked into the room where everyone was going to have breakfast, I thought to myself: It's impossible! On a Saturday morning, this volume of energy is amazing.

I greeted various colleagues, placed the fruit I'd bought on the table, and we all sat down to eat together. It was a lovely, relaxed atmosphere, with small talk and laughter. At 9 am, we were full of food, but still excited to get on with the day. It was incredible because even I was feeling hyped up and ready to go when I didn't feel like that before I stepped into the building.

My trainer got up from the table and gestured for me to follow; our day was just about to start. We walked a minute down the corridor and turned left into the usual room we use. I made myself comfortable at the table. As he turned around, I addressed him:

"This is my homework, Mr. Trainer," I handed it over to him and smiled.

He took the homework from me and glanced down at it. Looking back at me, he replied:

"Why do you call me Mr. Trainer? You can call me Lue, or Mr. Lee." He introduced himself to me and told me more about himself.

Lue was half Chinese and half Canadian; his mother was from Alberta, Canada and his father was from China; they met when his father immigrated to Canada 45 years ago. Lue is fairly tall, about the average height. When he stretches, you can still see his muscles, even when he is wearing his suit. His health and physique are extremely important to him, and so he's very careful about what he eats and drinks. At the office, he always has his water bottle with him, and only occasionally drinks hot drinks. Can you imagine this? He always drinks 2-3 liters a day, and that's probably at a minimum. I've realized that I've found his talks easy to follow and intriguing. His voice is always modulated with frequent, convenient pauses; they help to give me time to take in what he's saying and digest the concepts he mentions and explains.

I focused back on what was going on in the room; from what I can see of the window from my seat, it looked set to be an overcast day, with seemingly no break in the clouds. I felt sorry for the Sun, shining so lovely and bright earlier on, but now has had to hide behind the clouds. I half jolted awake and realized that I had started daydreaming by accident. I focused back on Lue; looking at him, I noticed the slight roundness of his face, with the small eyes and tiny wrinkles hiding behind his glasses. Luckily, he hadn't noticed that I wasn't concentrating for a split second. I nodded at him in confirmation that I had heard and understood what he had said. Sometimes that really is all that's needed to show that you understood — or that's how I felt anyway. And I did understand.

Mr. Lee, as I referred to him as now, paused for a moment, stretched his arms (I heard a few cracks of his bones), and then continued on with his talk. I was all ears, notebook on the table, lapping up every piece of information that he was giving me. It was very good advice. To be honest, all of his advice and teachings I have found to be very useful.

"Let's get to the subject of our fourth lesson together. We will look at your homework a little later on in the day. Today, we are talking about passion. So, coming here this morning, to the office, have you noticed that it's not like every other day? Did you spot what was different and uncommon in comparison to our normal work routine?"

I didn't need to think about my answer. I already knew it. I answered him straight away. "Yes, there was a huge difference when I came into the office this morning. I didn't expect it at all. As soon as I walked through the door, I felt this huge, unbelievable wave of energy and enthusiasm in the office. It was like everyone was eager to start the day, and it made me eager and excited. I've always found, myself included, that a lot of people prefer not to work and would much rather sleep and relax at the weekend. Most of the people have done a lot of work in their five-day working week, from Monday to Friday, and so they have two days to recharge their batteries so they are refreshed and ready to go back to work on Monday. People here seem to have a different mindset. They've shown up to the office this morning like they're doing their favorite thing to do and they're full of pride. They enjoyed it. You can see the difference quite clearly."

"Yes, that's completely right." He sat down opposite me and leaned back on his chair — not too far back that it was dangerous, but enough to stretch his back out. He *put his hands behind his head, probably because he felt a little lax today. It is Saturday, after all. He carried on. "Yes, they're all very passionate. In the dictionary, passion means "strong and barely controllable emotion." Similarly in business, it is the same feeling that a person has for their career. This is why you cannot compare business people, to those just working in jobs; business individuals use their logic as all of their decisions are made by using the logic they have. Their passion drives them forward to succeed in business, whatever they do is fuelled by passion but based on logic, and backup with their logic and emotions."*

Entrepreneurs do things based on logic back up by emotions.

He paused for a breather, adjusted his position in the chair, crossed his legs and continued: "This is why all of the big moves in the world that are regarding business and employment have been done by entrepreneurs and people who look at the business with passion. Imagine this: what if we go to the office where people are nagging about their job, and it's those people who are extremely happy when they have a weekend off work or have booked off a holiday. Those TGI Fridays and I hate Mondays; how far could we go? Every business has its ups and downs, they will always have good days and bad days, the best days and the worst days. There will always be failures alongside the victories, and it's important to remember that. But who is going to survive? I'll tell you who. Other than those select people who are passionate, no one will survive. These people never fully tire from working 12-15 hours a day, sometimes this is for their entire life without any break.

"Without passion, you can't overcome these things! To these business people, their career isn't just a job, it's a lifestyle. Everything they see and everything they do, they view everything as a note in an orchestral symphony.

They're the conductor, the one in control who conducts the highs and lows, controls the rhythm, tone, volume, and pace of the notes with short and long pauses. Everyone stands up and applauds the conductor and musician at the end of the piece, which is how they know they did a fantastic job, with some audiences standing and applauding at the end — which is a standing ovation. This is a very important point that you need to understand fully, with every fiber of your being, with every single cell in your body. That's if you want to be a successful entrepreneur, because in my opinion, the ultimate goal of any businessman or businesswoman, is to be an entrepreneur.

It should be a huge part of their life, and they need to work so hard to get it. They need to wake up and think about what their goals are, how they're going to achieve them, and how to become a successful entrepreneur.

Entrepreneurship is not a job

It's a life style

WHEN I WAS BORN

"Entrepreneurs wake up with their passion to make a change, and it's this passion that they live with for their whole lives. It's there with them all day long, even at night when they go to sleep, dream about it during the night, and then the next morning, they wake up thinking of their goal and run the next day with their passion. And this cycle will carry on, day in, day out for the rest of their lives. I think this will be enough for today," his tone changed slightly. I looked up from my notebook I was scribbling in, surprised that after only a few hours, I got to go home. I remained silent, waiting for him to carry on, and he did, after a lengthy pause.

"There is no homework or task for you to complete for tonight. What I will ask of you, for tonight, is just have a little think. It shouldn't take up too much time, but I do admit that thinking can sometimes be a hard thing to do at times, especially when you've worked so hard and you probably don't want to think about work while you're at home. I want you to think about your passion and your business. If money didn't matter, and it wasn't your main motivation for running your own business, then what would you be eager to do in this world? If you had no money issues, you had all the money you needed to live, you had everything you've ever wanted and you could live

the rest of your life doing whatever you wanted to do or to do nothing and have everything, what would you do just purely for you to enjoy?" He paused, leaving me deep in thought; I pondered his questions, but then he continued asking more, which snapped me back out of my thoughts.

"In which part of the world can you make a change in, and how? If you have to work 365 days a year, 24 hours a day, what would you do? You would live it, breathe it, and think about it all the time. To think about those questions, you should imagine yourself in La La Land, where everything is possible, and there are no obstacles to your success. Nothing is in your way there, there's nothing to prevent you from succeeding, from going down the path that you want to take. I would say this is kind of 'homework', but just think about it, don't write anything down. I hope you can get to the root and cause of your passions by Monday, and also recharge and spend some time with your family. Thank you for coming in so much this week; your commitment and dedication have been up to scratch and fantastic."

I packed away my things and got up from the table. I shook his hand, said goodbye and headed out towards the reception, and then outside to my car in the car park. I sat down in my car, and a wave of exhaustion hit me like a tsunami. It has been a very long week. As much as it has given me a lot more insight and has taught me a lot of things, I couldn't wait to go home and see my family. And do some thinking.

I'd messaged ahead to my wife that I was coming home earlier than I expected. As I unlocked the front door, I stepped inside to see my wife and son at the dining table eating a late lunch. She spotted me and smiled, pointing to a plate on the kitchen counter, which I presumed was mine, considering she already had a plate in front of her. I thanked her, grabbed the plate and joined them both at the table. I didn't expect her to have prepared lunch, so it was really nice to find that she had already prepared some for me.

Day 5

The big difference between the successful people and the public

Monday morning came too soon, and I woke to grisly grey clouds, spitting rain and a son who didn't want to get up out of bed again. On the plus side, I woke up on time and felt refreshed and energized for the day. I made a packed lunch, drank coffee whilst I persuaded my son to get dressed, which wasn't that hard considering his usual stubbornness. And while the weather outside was miserable, all three of us were in good spirits. We were going along our usual schedule and we were on time, and actually even slightly early for a change. I dropped my son off, then my wife, planted a kiss on her cheek as she got out of the car, to which she smiled at. I drove to the office humming a tune from the radio, but I couldn't tell you which one as they do sound similar when you don't know the songs.

The receptionist looked a little tired this morning, but she brightened up a little as I greeted her with great enthusiasm. I walked on through to the usual meeting room; a few people walked past and we all said our greetings. They weren't as cheerful as yesterday, but they were still in a good mood. Lue's door was wide open when I reached it, so I went straight in and greeted him with a lot of energy.

"Good morning Lue, how was the rest of your weekend?"
I almost shouted at him, as I walked through the
doorway.

Despite Mr. Lee being sat at the table facing the door, he
was looking down at the paperwork on the table and
didn't notice me until I almost shouted. He jumped
slightly, surprised that I had greeted him so loudly and
that I was in a good mood. Nevertheless, he responded
equally as jolly.

"Good morning. You're in high spirits today. It was good,
I did spend quite a lot of quality time with my family, and
I also managed to relax quite a bit as well. I read a book
and watched a movie. What about you?"

I sat down in my usual place as I replied. "Mine was good,
I've been thinking a lot as you've asked me to, and
worked on my homework a bit more, then just spent the
rest of it with my family. By the way, did you just say you
watched a movie? I'm only asking because I've heard that

successful people do not watch TV, in fact, most of them mentioned TV as a wasting time machine." I looked up at him as I said this and saw he was quite surprised. "Do you not believe the same thing?"

Mr. Lee smiled as he explained. It was clear that he didn't anticipate this question being asked, or doing my research this in-depth. "Yes, and no. It really does depend. So, I understand what you mean completely. So this is where my thought pattern comes into it. I do not watch TV as a hobby, I always watch it with a purpose or goal in mind. I also restrict myself from watching TV all the time. I don't waste my time watching TV that's pointless, but this also means that I choose good movies. I choose them not based on social media recommendations or just because some of the members of the public have suggested it. What I do instead, is look at the watched list of successful people as well as the people I follow, watching things on TV that would bring value to me, my family and my career. I never watch just anything to fill my time, I watch to nourish my mind and soul.

"Bingo! Now I feel better because I was thinking from now on, I can't enjoy my life as other people do."

"No, it's really not the way you think. The big difference between the successful people and the public is the way they both act. People with goals and a determination to succeed and a career in the future, do everything on purpose. They see, read, plan with intention themselves; they live life how they want. However, on the other hand, ordinary people live the life of others. Do you get what I mean? They see, read and act on others' choices; they follow the crowd, not their passion and they mostly (not all, might I add) do not have a determined brain. How is that? Are those explanations clear enough?"

"Oh, I see now. Thank you for enlightening me. I wish I had met you 10 years ago. Everything would have been so different for me. Definitely a lot different, and it would be better for me."

"You say that but what if it doesn't work out that way though? I guarantee that you were not ready 10 years ago for this. You were not ready for these concepts and your mind was certainly not prepared - that's for certain." He stood up, stretched and yawned, before continuing on. *"Would you like some coffee? I'm going to pop to the coffee machine in the kitchen to grab one for myself. It's*

definitely time for a little break. I can make tea as well if you would prefer?"

"Oh yes, can I have a coffee, please? I need to be a lot more focused these days. Can you put some sugar in it too?"

"Okay, I'll be back in a few minutes." He got up from the table and proceeded to make his way out of the room and to the kitchen, leaving me with my own thoughts for a while. A huge silence had fallen on the room in those few minutes Mr. Lee was gone. I could feel my thoughts sinking me into them, but my attention snapped back to the room when he came back into the room, bringing the beautiful scent of coffee with him.

"Coffees are ready." He placed mine down on the table, while he held his.

"Thank you. Right, I am ready to go back to our unfinished conversation, if you are?" I asked, suddenly full of energy now that my trainer has walked back into the room.

"Oh for sure, this is the conversation, if I'm correct, about you wishing to hear the concept 10 years ago? As I said earlier, you were not ready at the time. Do not forget that when the student is ready, the teacher is there for the student, him or her; this is the law of nature. You can only find the answer to this question in your head and your mind; so to try and find it, when you had never thought about the question, let alone 10 years ago. Imagine now you are here, and eager to learn, but out there is a lot of people whose ambition to learn and grow is not as big as yours. They do not look for it as you do, so they cannot find it."

I was a little confused so I asked him to explain it more. "So, you mean that the ability to ask the right questions is the treasure of their future. What I'm getting from this is I should be working on myself so I can strengthen my skills and ask the right questions. I will work on it and have a think later on at home, and I will bring my questions to you tomorrow. I need your guiding help though, may I have it?"

"It would be my pleasure," Lue said, drinking his coffee. "Let me know when they are ready. Okay, now, let's move

on to our topic of the day: being agile. To define the term, agile means to be able to move quickly and easily, and it has the same meaning in the business world as well.

"A lot of people want to start their business to become their own boss. That is fine, but in the end, most people tend to forget one simple concept. Because they want to do everything, everything becomes slower and therefore they lose big clients mostly because of what they're doing. These people wait until everything is perfect, but if they carry on waiting and waiting for the perfection to come, they will try and progress at a point where it's too far gone. Nowadays, with the rapid development rate of technology, people are pushed more and more to go faster. You do not have the time to make everything perfect before you start." He paused and allowed a few moments for me to put down my pen and to pick up my coffee to finish my drink. He politely waited until I had taken my last gulp and put my cup down, before carrying on his talk.

"Agility is a key factor to every business out there, no matter what your services and products are, who your target demographic (customers), and your business plan. Agility is the factor that is needed the most in any part of your business journey to become an entrepreneur.

Actually, some of the successful entrepreneurs achieve what they want, not just because they're smart or have good ideas; their company's growing but not because they have a featured product or fibular service, but all of it is because of their ability to move and act fast, faster than other people in their industry.

"So, with the agility strategy, you can be miles ahead of the others, but always proceed with caution. Going fast means that there's not much time to plan or do any research, but it gives you the path of no delay. Another benefit of increasing speed is that it prevents you from having so much doubt. If you aren't going fast, or they're delayed, this will cause doubts. Okay, this is as far as I can go as I've explained this concept enough. It is definitely a more practical theory than just a theatrical one. Please bear this concept in mind along the way of your business journey."

Act as fast as you can and check it where you can speed up your movements and your actions

WHEN I WAS BORN

Without a pause this time, Mr. Lee called it quits for the day. I didn't blame him; we've been here for hours and I was getting restless. When I stop focusing as much, I become a fidget, and I think I was about to start fidgeting when Mr. Lee called it a day.

"Okay, I do believe that we should leave it there for today. Don't forget to keep thinking which is your only homework, and let's continue this tomorrow morning at 10 am. Have a wonderful and productive day."

"I appreciate it, Mr. Lee, you're the best. See you tomorrow."

On the drive home, I didn't feel that tired, surprisingly; the working atmosphere has motivated me for sure, so I couldn't wait to spend some quality time with my family. Even though I had been losing focus back in the office, the cold breeze I felt around my face as I walked to my car has woke me up, so now I'm quite alert. I played lego with my son and tucked him into bed around 7:30 pm. Normally he sits through a short story every night before falling asleep, but tonight, he fell asleep halfway through.

After I checked that he was fast asleep, I did some thinking about the homework and then went to spend time with my wife. I even went to bed a little later, seeing as I could go into the office an hour later.

Day 6

Mastermind Group

Although, by the time that Tuesday rolled around, I was awake at my usual time; there went my chance for a lie-in. I got up as usual and went out of my normal morning routine. I'd had a dream, incidentally, it was the one thing that woke me up in the end, so I felt extra time at the office wouldn't be a bad idea. I decided to drop my wife and son off, and head straight to the office before I was supposed to get there (at 10 am) instead of heading back home. It turned out that I was going to be there before 9 am, so I didn't expect anyone to be in the office before 9 am.

I waved to the receptionist, who appeared to look slightly more tired than yesterday, who waved back but with not much enthusiasm. Walking on through past the reception area, I decided to make myself a coffee. I turned left into the kitchen, where a few of my other colleagues were. We greeted each other and I walked over to the coffee machine. After pressing a few buttons, the machine hummed to life and buzzed as the coffee poured out of the machine. With my cappuccino, I headed towards Mr. Lee's office to set up my pens and notebook. I was surprised to discover that he was already in there, I presumed that because he said a late start that had something important to do in the morning.

Mr. Lee spotted me walking in and grinned. "Good morning Mr. Trainee, I see you're here an hour earlier than what you were supposed to be. I'm curious. May I ask why?"

"Good morning Mr. Lee. Thank you for asking. My dream woke me up this morning, and I became excited and I couldn't get back to sleep. My dream pushed me to come into the office early to socialize and network with other people here; I want to learn from them as well, and hear their experiences in business."

"We called this group Mastermind, Mastermind Group Member. It's very good to hear that we have you in our group. Now off you go and mingle with your colleagues. Then I will meet you at 10 am in this very room. Excellent progress."

"Thank you, Mr. Lee. I will see you in just under an hour."
I walked back out into the hallway and glanced in the next
room, where there were a few colleagues having a little
chat. At first, I stood there listening, but eventually joined
in the conversation when I had something to contribute
to the talk. We had some great chitchat. Everyone was
bursting with energy and excitement about what they do
every day when they come into this office. Everyone has
their goals, ambitions, and missions; they all offer very
different types of services, but the general consensus is
that every single one of them wants to make changes in
the world - be it a big change or a small change. This
could be within their communities, their countries or
around the world.

In each mastermind member's room, there are a lot of
positive quotes and paperwork covering the four walls of
the room, with their goals written on the walls too. There
are goal sheets, vision boards, mission statements,
certificates, achievements, and rewards. This was a very
positive office, and I quite liked it.

On their desks, there was a picture of their loved ones,
trophies, a small statue, certificates, daily chores, their
laptops, and their team picture. It is obvious that they're
such a tight-knit team. Spending an hour getting to know

the people in that office has helped me with how I should set up my room and office, what is needed and where I want to put some of the objects.

With five minutes to spare, I was outside Mr. Lee's room. He spotted me and said, "Come in." So I did.

"Hello there, again, Mr. Lee," I sat back down at the table.

"How was your morning so far? Did you manage to mingle with other people?" He asked and it was like he was reading my mind.

"It's awesome, I learned a lot from the people; you said their group name was - what was it? Ah, yes I remember Mastermind. It's like I can see myself with them, have my office with them and my future."

It was at this point that Mr. Lee began to get excited. "Yes, yes, you are right. In fact, it is my topic for today. I called this group Master-Mind because everyone thinks the same way. They all help each other to grow so much while part of this group.

"One of the most important rules that you must follow in order to be successful, is that you should surround yourself with great people. Imagine this: you want to climb a cliff, who would you associate with to get information? Who do you ask for help? How do you find out about what you need? You only need to trust the people who have already mastered cliff climbing. For being an entrepreneur, the best people you need the most are the entrepreneurs or people who study them and do research on them. Find those personalities, and spend more time with them. Do you know a lot of people like them?" He posed all of these questions to me, and I had no choice but to contemplate silently for a full minute before responding.

"Yes I do, but there are problems involved with this as some of them I can't talk to or meet up with them because they are very far from me. Even those who are close to me, I'm sure they do not have time to meet me. What should I do?" The forgotten frustration at this fact started to rise in my throat. I mentally pushed it back.

"I understand your point, but you can read their books, blogs, and you can watch their videos or listen to their podcast. These actions help you to read their minds and their ideas. Besides that, some of them have what they learned and experienced in the formats of webinars, seminars, video training. You can buy them and use them as you see fit."

He leaned back in his chair, looked up at the ceiling and said. "Now I want to talk about another topic as well today. Most employees who want to transition to the owner of a business feel weakness in the topic. In fact, there are two topics, not one, that we should discuss. They are money and sales, and the two are much related. Have you ever had an employee complain about sales when they're not a salesperson, or hate to sell something?" I didn't think he wanted a response, but I realized after a moment that he did.

"Yes, I do. Not only is one of my employees like that, but I'm like this myself. I can't sell."

"I see. Let me ask you a question, as an employee in your workplace, what do you trade money for? One hour of your time? Your knowledge? Your experience? Do you think you can trade it with your wage? Isn't it a type of sales? Have you seen anybody who can get a better connection with your boss with less skill and time make more money than you? Do you think he or she can sell his/her time and skills better than you?"

"Oh my God! You are right, I've not seen it like this before. It's really interesting." I began scribbling down notes again in my notebook. I shivered, thinking that the room has become a lot colder. I was thinking about putting on my jacket. It was that cold.

"Every one of us here is a salesperson, whether you like it or not. We sell our time, skills, emotions, and other things — you get the idea. In fact, we are all traders. If we can trade better we gain more, and money is the cheapest part of our trades. Do you know what the most expensive trade is?"

I frowned, thinking deeply. It didn't take long before a lightbulb went off in my head. "Time?"

"Yes. Time is the most valuable thing to trade. That's why as an entrepreneur, it's essential for you to learn how to manage your time effectively. Knowing how to use each second of your day will be blessed in your future. Back to our topics. Money is like a reward for how good you were at your job. It is also your entrepreneurship fuel; the more fuel you have means you can go faster and further." He took a deep breath. "Though it's gone by quick today, I think I'm going to leave it here and we can continue where we left off tomorrow. So, in terms of homework, what do you think it is?"

I laughed and said "Printing money?"

He chuckled and answered, "Yes, you end up printing that money as your homework, and I'll see you in jail then."

Then we both laughed loudly for a solid few minutes. Mr. Lee threw his head in laughter, his chest rising and exhaling rapidly. It took us a while to calm down and cease our laughter. By the end of it, I had tears in my eyes from laughing too much.

"Seriously though," my trainer tried to keep his voice level. "Tonight's homework is done by using the chart that I give you; you need to identify every type of revenue that has come into your business and identify what activities bring money directly to your business. These should be the main activities of your daily routine. The chart sheet will help you to complete this, and it's on my desk over there, so pick it up on your way out. I hope you have a relaxing evening tonight, and I will see you first thing tomorrow."

He stayed sitting down as I shook his hand, packed away my stuff and picked up the chart sheet from his desk. I addressed him once again before I left the room. "Staying late tonight?"

He looked up from the paperwork he was filling out. "A little. I need to get some of this paperwork done. Go on, go and enjoy yourself, and do the homework." He grinned before putting his head back down to concentrate on his task.

By the time that I got home, my wife had cooked dinner for us three and was just adding the finishing touches when I walked in the door. She smiled at me, and I was in such a good mood, that I went over to her and hugged her, spinning her around in a little dance twirl. She laughed loudly, pleased by my actions.

"Come on, let me finish. Dinner's nearly ready."

"Okay, okay. Do you need a hand before I sit down?" My wife is already busying herself by adding the sauce to the dinner. The aroma of the food made my mouth water. I hadn't realized how hungry I was.

"Huh? Oh no, no it will be two minutes."

So now that I knew I didn't need to give a hand, I went and sat down at the dinner table, ruffling our son's hair as I passed him. He squealed with delight, so I played with him whilst we had time before dinner. It was great to hear him laugh, and be here at home. It was the start of a great evening doing nothing but spending time with my wonderful family and doing the homework. However, after dinner, my wife said that we needed to do the shopping. I agreed that we did need to go shopping, for food and other household items. So, instead of completing the homework, we had to go shopping instead. I felt a little bad, but I did some of the work before we went, but nowhere near enough. I thought to myself as we got into the car, that I would do some work when we got back. By the time we arrived back home and unpacked the shopping, I was too exhausted to think about work and the business. It was the one time that I felt too tired to do the homework. I decided to go to bed slightly earlier than usual so that I can get enough rest for tomorrow's day at work. I fell asleep quickly and ended up in a heavy dreamless sleep.

Day 7

Research the Market

Wednesday morning started like any other day; the weather was overcast and I dropped off my wife and son on time. So I was a tad early when I pulled into the parking lot but decided to head into the building anyway. It was the part-time receptionist on the desk today; she smiled and asked how I was, and we made polite small talk before I tore away to make a coffee. Mr. Lue's office was open by the time I got there with my cappuccino, so I went in and prepared myself for the day; he wasn't there just yet, for a change, but five minutes later, Mr. Lue showed up in the doorway, a little out of breath. I didn't say anything until he had settled down and caught his breath.

"Good morning," he said. "Quite the early bird, aren't you?"

"I am, indeed," I said. "I wake up energized every morning and motivated to come into work. It's a good feeling. I felt like this especially this morning," I stretched my arms above my head; I was raring to go for the day. I don't even think I need a coffee just yet either, and that's unheard of for me.

WHEN I WAS BORN

"That sounds great," He said, getting out his laptop and blue folder from his bag. "How was your afternoon yesterday?" This was his routine question every morning, without fail. I like how it has settled down into a routine now, I'm really getting back into the swing of things now I'm working.

"It was good, not much work done, unfortunately. I came home and ate food, then we went shopping — me, my wife and my son. So I've not had time to do all of the business activities. I am sorry, I can finish it during the time here today or do it tonight for definite."

I felt so bad now, so full of shame and I was hoping Mr. Lee would let this slide. I am still very motivated, it's just family life came first last night, when it needed to. I tensed, waiting for Mr. Lee's response. It's not one that I expected. I was pleasantly surprised.

Mr. Lee took his eyes from his laptop to look at me, his expression was soft. He said: "That sounds like a very *good evening to me. First of all, as a balanced entrepreneur myself, I know that you have to have a balanced life. Spending quality time with your family is one of the best and most important parts of your life, and you shouldn't miss that for the world. Besides, when you do go out shopping, you can also do your research at the same time. Remember what we talked about a week ago?"*

"Research? I can? How can I do that?" I asked, my mouth hanging open slightly. I had no idea that I could do this. I'm pretty sure he's never mentioned when it would be a good time to conduct the research. I better take some good notes, and maybe do it when we go shopping next week.

"Yes, your research. It's quite simple really," he replied with confidence in his voice. You can identify who is your target market. Where are those people? Are they out every day for shopping?"

"Yes, they are." It started to make a little sense. But I still felt like he needed to explain more. I sipped away at my

coffee, which was beginning to go slightly cold. I didn't mind though, I wanted to drink the coffee so that it could give me the energy back that I had at the beginning of the day. I'd started to lose the energy a little bit. These talks are tiring me out constantly.

"As a businessman, if you do not know people, you can not deal with them or sell your product or service to them. As well as the tools that businessmen have to help them get to know people, watching them through their daily activities is the best way to know and understand their emotions. This way you can spend time with your family and do your research as well. Depending on your business, you can even find new opportunities out there as well. Today we will now look at and discuss different ways for you to research the market."

With a grunt, Mr. Lee got out of the chair opposite me and stood up. He cracked his hands as he headed over to the bookshelves at the back of the room, to the left of the whiteboard that we hadn't used in a few days. It still had remnants of Mr. Lee's writing from one of our previous sessions. It had faded slightly, so I couldn't really tell from what day it had come from. Realizing that he had a book missing from his shelves, he wordlessly glanced around the room to try and locate it. I watched him in silence the whole time. When he realized that he had left the missing book on his desk, he sauntered over to it to pick it up, and then consequently returning it to its original place on the bookshelf. He must have had several shelves and bookcases filled with books in this corner of the room, I mused. How he must have read all of them is beyond me. Still, as I watched this big man search all of his shelves and bookcases for the book he wanted to show me, I drank the remainder of my now-cold coffee, glancing over to where his water bottle stood on the other side of the table. It was a two-liter bottle and was already half empty. It was only 10 in the morning and he'd already drunk that much water — it's insane. Well, I was presuming that he wanted to show me a book. Maybe he just remembered he needed one for later on, and right now I'm just sitting here waiting for him to find out.

After several minutes of searching for a book, in complete silence, Mr. Lue found it back in the first bookcase on the left; one that he had supposedly searched several times. I heard a big sigh, as he made his way back to the meeting table where I was sitting patiently waiting for him. I looked at his face; he didn't seem to be in a bad mood because of it, he seemed perfectly relaxed and ready to carry on.

He sat back down in his chair and carried on as if the past five minutes never happened. And no, we didn't need the book for our talk. I presume he fetched the book so that he didn't forget it later on.

"As I've mentioned previously to you, going to the market and watching and observing is personally one of the best ways to understand people's pain and gains. You can do it personally or you can hire people or a company to do the market research for you. Let me just mention that all research that you carry out should be based on observations and not any judgment. So to explain this a bit better, I categorized the research into two main methods. The first method is physical research and the second is virtual research.

"To explain them in further detail, I will do the following. For physical research, we conduct and carry out the research based on physical existence and research. This just means that the researchers have a few ways to gather information i.e. anonymous shoppers, physical questionnaires and surveys, interviews, etc, there are many more ways to gather the research you need, but these are the main ways that are most popular amongst a lot of entrepreneurs.

"So in the case of anonymous shoppers: it's done by us or another individual but the people who are doing it should have these qualities: a great memory to answer the questions after their shopping experience; should be honest and trustworthy, it's obvious and there's no need to explain because you are going to make your decision based on what they have said; they should be detailed oriented and have the ability to observe everything without being noticeable and they must have good writing skills to write down everything and report about the shopping experience.

"So, the physical questionnaire and survey: this may be the hardest one as we would need to make people fill out the survey or questionnaire in their location. Not everyone will want to fill out a survey and a lot of people will ignore the survey or questionnaire, which is why this *is the most difficult method of researching your customers. Although it is difficult, it can still be a good method of research.*

"Be sure to write this down because I want to tell you some very important tips about people's shopping," Mr. Lee looked up at me, ensuring that I was with him so far and that I had understood everything he had currently said. I paused my writing to confirm this, looked up at him and smiled. So far, this was making sense to me.

"I have written every single word you have said so far on this," I said. "I intend to make notes on everything you say." I was going to have to get a new notebook soon at this rate; this one was already half full. I liked it though, and made a quick mental note to myself to remind myself to type up the notes I've made — just in case something happened to the notebook, and I had to refer back to my notes a few years down the line. I can now see why he said that this advice would last me for the whole time of running a business. I can see myself looking back at these notes in different periods of my life, and this is why I'm making really good notes and paying a lot of attention to every word Lue is saying.

Satisfied with the answer I'd given, he nodded and carried on. "People tend to always make their decision based on their emotions and not based on their logic, but when you want to do the survey or ask them to answer the questionnaire, they use their rational side of their brain. So your paper is filled out using the person's logic when you need them to use their emotions to fill out the survey. While the survey isn't that useful in the long run, you could, however, still use it as a source. You can glean some good information from them either way.

"Interviews can be compared to the questionnaire but with one major difference: rather than the questions printed on paper for someone to potentially answer them (and using their logic rather than emotions), but it is based on an actual conversation that has been had in real life. The conversation would happen between the researcher and the shopper and would help with getting more of an emotional response from the shoppers. When drawing comparisons to the surveys and questionnaires, it's a lot more accurate, because you can tell what they think. Furthermore, it is also easier to read the emotions of the interviewee though it does come with a possible risk of inaccuracies, which some may deem worth it in the *grand scheme of things. It's definitely a viable option, amongst the others that are out there.*

So these are some of the physical market research methods that have been done time and time again and have proved to be successful. There is a lot to learn by doing these methods, especially a lot to learn about your customers or potential customers. They were less costly to do if you did them yourself rather than hire someone else out to help you conduct the research. However, they may not be new enough for the market these days, so you might have difficulty finding the research for the exact market you ideally want, or for the exact product or service that you provide. Are you still with me, Mr. Trainee?" Mr. Lee changed the subject quite drastically, and I felt like he just saw me frozen like a statue, just staring at him as he spoke.

"Of course I am, Mr. Lee. I'm listening to every word you say. But I must admit, that my focus has started to dwindle — only slightly though, but I am in need of a coffee. It feels like I'm drowning in my own thoughts, imagining all the ways that I can do some successful market. I'm going to make one if you would be kind

enough to excuse me. Would you like a cup as well? I don't mind making two cups. I am sure you will probably want some."

"Yes please," he smiled. So off I went. For the first mid-session, I was venturing into the kitchen to make coffee instead of him. It was a huge sign that I was getting settled into this new job, and I liked it. There was one woman in the kitchen just finishing up her black coffee. She smiled at me as she walked out. Pouring the coffee, I decided to go for an americano this time, but with milk, and I got a flat white for Mr. Lee.

Stepping back into the room with two cups of coffee in my hand, I already felt slightly energized from the walk to the kitchen and social interaction. I definitely feel a lot more comfortable in this office, and even in the building itself. I knew and have interacted with most of the people who work there.

As I sat back down, I turned to my trainer. "Are you going to explain the second method of research now? Virtual research?"

He nodded and decided to carry on with the talk. I realized that the time is now around lunchtime or the afternoon, but I wasn't that hungry.

"Virtual research is based on online and web-based materials. We have just about everything we need, it's the same as physical research but it's all online, which is the biggest difference. It looks a lot easier to do, but it still has its pros and cons. So, there's good news and bad news. The good news is you can use more of the different methods of research. However, the bad news is you have to use different research methods because none of them are really complete and accurate. You need to combine them until you get your desired and accurate results. My recommendation is to use as many methods of two types of research-based upon your budget. Of course, nothing is free. With these ways, you will know more about your market and your competitors. Do you have any questions about today's topic?"

"Do I need to run the research one time or do I need to research my market regularly?" I asked, drinking my second cup of coffee today. I started to perk up and become more lively halfway through the coffee.

"That's a very good question, so well done for thinking of and asking of it. As everything changes by time, your customers, their value, and their needs will change soon. So you should do it on a regular basis to avoid this. Some companies have research departments that do their research every day, but of course, this wouldn't be likely in your circumstances when you are just a small business yourself. I am sure you can not do it like them and now it should be done by yourself in the beginning but as you go further in the path you will be able to outsource it. Who knows, maybe one day soon you will have a research department in your company. Who knows? It could well happen if you keep striving for these goals."

I just smiled at him, while I was imagining myself running a huge firm that has an individual research department. That would be a dream come true if that were to happen. Though I know I must work really hard to make this happen. Now that I'm off in this dream la la land, it's very difficult to snap out of it. Though, it must be time to go quite soon. I didn't pay attention to the very last thing he'd just said, so I snapped out of my thoughts to concentrate on the rest of his talk.

"Well, if you have no more questions, then we can bring today's session to a close. So you can complete the other homework as well, but I am going to give you some questions on market research as examples for you to do your research. I am sure you can find out more information as you think about your product and service. I wish you a good evening, and I hope that you rest up. We've had an incredibly intense day, what with all the descriptions of the types of research. I hope you've managed to create a decent set of notes. Right then," he got up from the chair and stretched. *"I won't keep you any longer. I will see you tomorrow Mr. Trainee."*

"Thanks a lot for today, it's been very insightful. Have a good evening and I will see you bright and early."

On the drive home, I was still deep in thought about where I want to take my business, and how big I could grow and develop it further. I snapped out of my thoughts, again, when I recognized the street I was driving down — my own! I can't believe that I'd driven all the way back and it didn't even feel like it. I parked up outside the house and sat there for about five minutes. I felt very tired and drained for no reason at all. I definitely got enough sleep last night, so maybe it was just the intense talk and learning I was doing today.

When I mustered the energy to get out of the car and enter the house, I realized that my wife instantly knew something was up. She stopped making dinner and came to me to ask what was wrong. I hugged her, greeted her and told her I was just feeling tired. She made me a cup of tea, and told me to go and sit down and rest with our son, and wait for dinner. After dinner, whilst she was sitting down and resting, I decided to make a fruit salad for dessert, to surprise her. I chopped up some bananas, apples, grapes, and peach, and topped it with some strawberry yogurt and pecan nuts. Safe to say, she absolutely loved it. I managed to get all of the homework done, in preparation for what I think is the last day of training. I retired to bed a little later than usual that night, as I'd been so determined to complete the homework.

Day 8

Last Day
I was feeling bittersweet.

Waking up wasn't great. I felt very groggy and tired, probably still tired from going to bed later than usual. The Sun was poking out from behind clouds and shining brightly for 7 am, but it didn't improve my mood one bit. It was the last day of our sessions, and I've begun to grow very fond of them over the past week, so I was feeling a bit bittersweet over it. Of course, they have to finish at some point, but I don't want them to finish just yet.

I was very reluctant to go to the office today, out of fear that this was the last time I'd be driving there. I didn't want to admit that this could all be over and I wasn't sure if these sessions could continue. But anyway, I had to be there for 9 am sharp. I reached the parking lot with two minutes to spare. It was clear that I was dragging my feet towards the building. I felt like I needed to see Lue every day. I had somehow become a little addicted to sitting in his office and listening to him talk, hanging onto every word that he said. But there was no choice, and today is our last day.

I half heartedly waved to the receptionist and didn't really register her response to my probably gloomy looking face. I made my way through to Mr. Lee's office, not wanting a coffee to start off the day. I walked in to find him sitting at the table, ready to start. I felt bad, not that I was late, but that I was coming in with this negative energy and sad outlook on our last session together. I dumped my bag down under the table, whilst I sat down in my usual chair, facing my trainer.

"Good morning Mr. Lue."

"Good morning. I can tell just by looking at you that today hasn't been very joyful for you, has it?" Busted. So he could read me like a book. I don't know what I expected. Of course, he was going to do that.

"Mr. Lee, I used to be here every day and learn new things and now today is the last day. It fills me with sadness. I want to keep coming here and listen to your wise words." I looked down at the table, embarrassed.

"Yes I know, but coming to the office and talking about different aspects of the business will not help you to establish yours, which is ultimately what you need to do now. Besides, we will have our monthly sessions to review what you have done and if there are questions that you have, I'll be here to help. Now, how does that sound to you?" A smile started to grow on my lips because of what he had said. It was like blood was pumping around my body faster.

"Sounds great Mr. Lue," I replied. I got out my notebook, ready to take on the last session and motivated to learn new things. My negativity has dissipated, and in its place is the positive energy that I've felt so many times before while I've been sitting in this very seat.

"Okay, so our topic today is teams. In fact, this topic is much related to the leadership topic which we discussed beforehand. But it is very essential to understand how important your team is in your business. Let's start as we did from the first day and run this session like a question and answer session. If this is okay with you and you agree that this would be the best format for our last official session for now, then feel free to start and fire away with the first question you have.

WHEN I WAS BORN

"Sure, I'm happy to do this until I run out of questions. In my business, should I start with just myself, and then add employees and team members later when my business grows and develops, or should I have a team from the beginning of my business?"

Mr. Lee was clearly impressed with my first question. So was I, to be honest. "That's a very smart question. I am glad that you asked. You can not climb the business ladder just by yourself. You need a team in order for you and your business to grow. Without them you could not grow, and you won't grow either. This team could be inside your organization or outside of your organization, as long as you outsource your tasks. But there should be a team no matter what. To answer your question on when you should start to hire other people for specific tasks, and when you should pay to outsource them to do those tasks for you, it's very practical and it is learnt solely by experience. The rule of thumb says you have to do the most essential, most important tasks of your business, especially the tasks that are related to the sales. Other than that, you have to give the other tasks to another person to do. You need to follow this cycle in every task."

Mr. Lee got up from his chair and went over to the whiteboard. Using the rag, he wiped off the old writing that was written during our sessions last week, and then he drew three boxes on the whiteboard, and wrote in them.

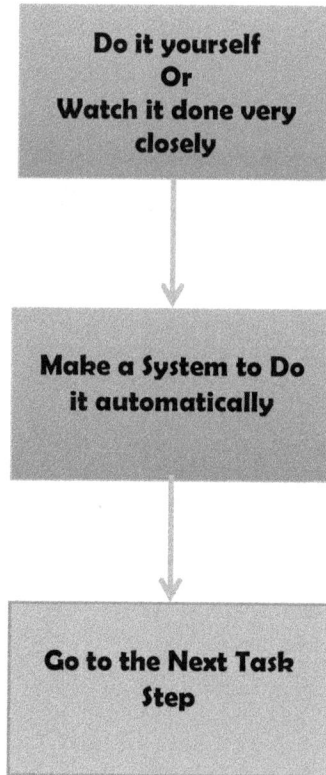

As he finished writing on the board, he put the marker cap back and continued talking where he stood. "As your business grows, you need to hire more people for management, operation, supervision, accountant, researchers, developers, consultant and a lot more. But to refer back to your question about if you should grow first and then hire someone? I can compare it to what came first, the chicken or the egg? There are many different approaches to this matter. You can experience this yourself or use other business owner's consultation. And sometimes it's worth it if you trust your guts! Now fire away and ask the next question."

Mr. Lee returned to his seat and waited for my next question. I finished up the last sentence in my notes and took a minute to think.

"Does my team need to have special skills, other than the one for which they are hired for?" I asked.

"Yes, they need to have a teamwork mentality and be able to work in a team very well. And if they don't, they will be facing huge challenges. Therefore, before hiring them you can ask about their past experiences about the teams they have been a part of, and how they found that. Do not ask what they will do on the team. In my opinion, in any hiring process, you want to interview a person and *ask about their past and not about the future. This is because they would talk about the future the way in which they think you'd want to hear it. If they were not a great team player, then there's a huge chance they never will be in the future. And I believe that is enough for the beginning and if you do not have any other questions then we can go forward before next time will come up and I am with you along the way to help you."*

"Thank you, Mr. Trainer, for everything."

"My pleasure, Mr. Trainee. Now let's focus on the action because, without action, a business plan is just a dream." He clapped his hands together, excited.

"Okay, so what is the next step?"

"Sales. Sales are the first, next, last and most important steps. Sales are the blood in the business. What would the body be without blood?"

"A dead body?"

"It's the same as in business. You must get prepared as fast as you can for sales. You know almost anything you need to know to start it off and you have the starting material package. You now know that the concepts and

the rest will be learned through your journey," he paused and looked directly at me with a smile on his face. "So, are you ready?"

Action is the most important part of an organization and sales is the most important action.

Note:

Note:

Note:

Note:

Note:

Note:

Note:

Mehdi Souroriayan Biography –

Mehdi was born in 1973 in Shiraz, Iran. He grew up with three younger siblings and was particularly close with his father, with whom he started a family business at age 18.

At age 24, Mehdi graduated with a degree in electrical engineering, before returning to the family business once more to open his first branch. Two years later, he married the love of his life.

At age 30, Mehdi managed to build a five-story building at one of his father's properties, despite having no practical architectural experience. To this day, he believes that this project and the experience he gained from it, taught him to be more courageous in all walks of life. After this, Mehdi and his wife moved to Canada while also welcoming a son into the world. Despite this, Mehdi still managed to find the time to open a new jewelry branch within his new home country. In Canada, he embarked on a new career in finance, while simultaneously managing his existing jewelry branches. In less than three years, Mehdi managed to build a team of over 20 trained agents. His Jewellery business has now evolved into one of the top jewelry branches in the city, holding several highly anticipated exhibition experiences. Not only is Mehdi the perfect businessman, but he has also proved to be the perfect husband and father across many years. He garners respect from his family and his team and is known as a great leader with superb empathy. Mehdi is humble and helpful to this day, still pushing himself with constant reading and investing part of his income into further educating both himself and his team. Mehdi strives for perfection and has achieved it in all walks of life.

www.ingramcontent.com/pod-product-compliance
Lightning Source LLC
Chambersburg PA
CBHW071426210326
41597CB00020B/3664